G000160526

BELAIR ACTIVE SCIENCE 4

Tony Laukaitis

Contents

Belair Publications

First published in 2000 by Belair Publications.
United Kingdom: Belair Publications, Albert House, Apex Business Centre, Boscombe Road, Dunstable, LU5 4RL.

Belair allows photocopying of pages marked 'copiable page' for educational use, providing that this use is within the confines of the purchasing institution. Copiable pages should not be declared in any return in respect of any photocopying licence.

© 2000 Belair Publications, on behalf of the author.

Belair books are protected by international copyright laws. All rights are reserved. The copyright of all materials in this book, except where otherwise stated, remains the property of the publisher and author. No part of this publication may be reproduced, stored in a retrieval system, or transmitted, in any form or by any means, for whatever purpose, without the written permission of Belair Publications.

Editor: Hayley Willer
Layout artist: Suzanne Ward
Cover design: Martin Cross
Illustrations: Virginia Gray (Graham-Cameron Illustration)

Every effort has been made to contact copyright holders of material used in this book. If any have been overlooked, we will be pleased to make any necessary arrangements.

British Library Cataloguing in Publication Data. A catalogue record for this book is available from the British Library.

Tony Laukaitis hereby asserts his moral right to be identified as the author of this work in accordance with the Copyright, Designs and Patents Act 1988.

ISBN 1 84191 073–2

Introduction

Active Science is a series of six books designed to be used with children aged five to eleven. The series provides teachers' notes and worksheets matched to the topics in the QCA Scheme of Work for Science.

Active Science 4 can be used alongside the QCA Scheme as the basis of a year's work or it can be used to supplement existing schemes of work already in place in school.

The activities included in the book are varied and challenging and encourage the children to think scientifically. The emphasis is on providing the children with first-hand experience of scientific practical work and investigation.

The book is split into eleven chapters. Each chapter consists of a teachers' page and three photocopiable worksheets. The teachers' page is split into the following sections.

Background – This provides the necessary background knowledge for teachers to deliver the topic.

Activity pages – This section contains:
- the main learning objectives in terms of knowledge, understanding and skills, for each activity, to help teachers with planning and assessment
- ideas for further activities
- guidance points for discussion
- safety warnings.

Oral work – This section provides opportunities for:
- discussion
- questioning that encourages children to think about the scientific process
- oral presentations
- interviewing
- inviting guest speakers into the classroom
- role-play.

Written work – This section provides ideas for written work, including:
- comparing and contrasting
- producing leaflets and guides on certain scientific issues
- planning investigations
- writing conclusions and explanations
- full scientific report writing.

ICT – A range of opportunities for the use of ICT in the Science Curriculum is provided, including:
- researching information using CD-ROM and the Internet
- using ICT programs to produce scientific information in the form of text and graphics
- using computer databases
- using data-handling packages to present results of experiments
- using audiotapes and videotapes to record work.

The photocopiable worksheets contain a variety of activities that provide opportunities for the children to do the following.

Plan – This includes:
- making predictions
- considering what evidence is to be collected
- planning investigations and fair tests.

Obtain and present evidence – This includes:
- making careful observations and measurements
- using simple apparatus
- choosing methods of recording
- recording results systematically.

Consider evidence and evaluate – This includes:
- making comparisons
- using results to draw conclusions
- explaining in terms of scientific knowledge and understanding
- considering whether a test is fair or not
- deciding how an investigation could be improved.

Skeleton and Muscles

Background

There are two main types of skeleton. Animals with a backbone (vertebrates) have their skeleton inside the body. Other animals (arthropods) have their skeleton outside the body (e.g. crabs, lobsters, spiders, insects, woodlice). Both internal and external skeletons give support and protection, and help with movement. External skeletons also stop animals drying up and keep out germs, but these animals can only grow by shedding their skins (outer skeletons). In vertebrates the skeleton grows inside the body, as the body grows.

The skeleton has joints so that you can move parts of your body. Muscles move joints. Muscles work in pairs, each pulling in opposite directions. One muscle pulls the joint one way, the other one pulls it back. Muscles are attached to bones by tendons. There are two main types of muscle: those that work automatically (e.g. heart, stomach, and diaphragm) and those that we control.

Activity pages

The Human Skeleton

Learning objectives
- To know that bones have different shapes and names.
- To know that some bones have special jobs.

At this stage the children do not need to know the bones' medical names. Ask the children to look at the shapes of the bones and relate the shape to their function. For example, the skull is a box shape to protect the brain; rib cage holds the heart and lungs; long bones in the legs aid running; small finger bones allow fine movement; backbone is made of 33 bones to allow movement.

Muscles and Bones

Learning objectives
- To know that bones have muscles joined to them.
- To know that to make a bone move a muscle must contract.
- To know that muscles work in pairs.

To bend a joint, a muscle gets shorter (contracts), but that muscle cannot get longer itself and push the joint back into place. Muscles can only work by pulling, so they are arranged in pairs. One muscle makes the bones move in one direction and the other makes them move in the opposite direction. The arm model shows this working. Notice in the model that the contracting muscle appears slack when shortening. In reality, this would be very tight to pull the other muscle into its relaxed position. Emphasise the point that as you bend the arm the elastic band (muscle) gets shorter (contracts) and pulls at the joint, making the bone move. The other elastic band (muscle) is stretched thinner (relaxes). At this level it is important that the children know that: 1. Muscles move bones 2. Muscles only move bones by pulling (contracting) and 3. Muscles work in pairs.

Animal Skeletons

Learning objectives
- To know that the skeleton helps protect the body parts.
- To know that some animals have a skeleton inside the body.

Point out similarities between skeletons: skull and ribs for protection; foot and finger bones for gripping; large bones to aid movement.

Safety – When looking at animal bones ensure they are cleaned.

Oral work

- Discuss a model skeleton or bones and build up a word bank to describe what they look like.
- Discuss similarities and differences between other vertebrate animal skeletons.
- Discuss the functions of the skeleton.
- Discuss keeping bones and muscles healthy through exercise and maintaining correct diet.
- Discuss bone problems: arthritis, breakages, slipped discs.
- Discuss how a child's skeleton differs from an adult's: joints on X-ray pictures show larger gaps where bones still have to form.
- Discuss if there are any animals without skeletons (e.g. slugs and worms).

Written work

Ask the children to write a paragraph entitled 'What is a joint?'. The three types of joint in the human body are grouped according to how they move: fixed joint (skull); slightly moveable joint (backbone); freely moveable joint (elbow, knee, hip, wrist). The children could explain the structure of a joint and how a joint reduces friction when bones move against each other.

ICT

Use CD-ROM or video to show muscle movement and skeletons of animals.

The Human Skeleton

 **Key Idea**   There are many different bones in the body.

1. Join the names to the correct bones on the skeleton.

Finger bones

Foot bones

Skull

Lower arm bones

Upper arm bones

Lower leg bones

Backbone

Pelvis

Thigh bones

Collarbones

Shoulder blades

Ribs

2. The names for the bones of the skeleton are all jumbled up. Rearrange the letters to identify them. Use the list above to help you.

a. ghiht beno _____

b. kulls _____

c. birs _____

d. werol ram ebons _____

e. nifreg noebs _____

f. toof snobe _____

g. slevip _____

h. repup mar nobe _____

i. cakboneb _____

j. slorehud lebad _____

k. rollacnoeb _____

l. worel gel obens _____

Muscles and Bones

You will need
- Yellow, blue and red crayons
- Scissors
- Two elastic bands (6cm long)
- Card
- Paper fastener
- Cotton thread
- Sticky tape
- Glue

Key Idea   Muscles are needed to move bones.

1. Read the following on how muscles work.

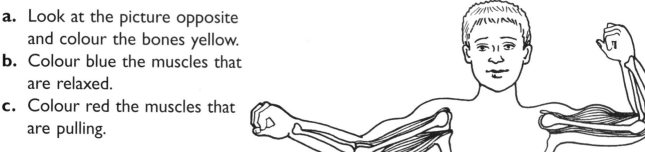

- Muscles cannot push.
- Muscles only pull.
- Muscles usually work in pairs when moving bones.
- One muscle will get shorter and pull the bone to its new position.
- The second muscle relaxes.
- To move the bone back, the second muscle will shorten and the first muscle will relax.

Contracts

Relaxes

a. Look at the picture opposite and colour the bones yellow.

b. Colour blue the muscles that are relaxed.

c. Colour red the muscles that are pulling.

3. Cut out the arm pieces below and glue them on to card.
Join the parts together with a paper fastener.
Attach cotton thread to the ends of the bands. Tape the thread into place as shown.

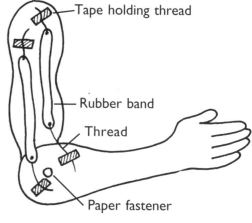

Tape holding thread

Rubber band

Thread

Paper fastener

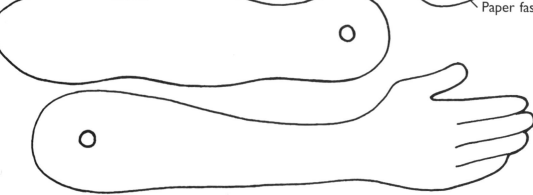

Animal Skeletons

 **Key Idea** Bones have many uses.

1. Look at the rabbit skeleton below and join each labelled bone to its job.

This protects the brain.

This protects the heart.

This supports the body.

These are used for jumping.

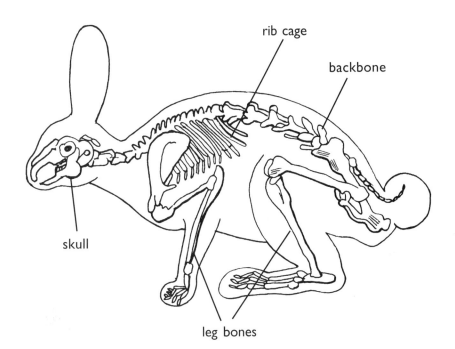

2. On each of the animal skeletons below, label:
   a. The skull
   b. The backbone
   c. The leg bones
   d. The rib cage

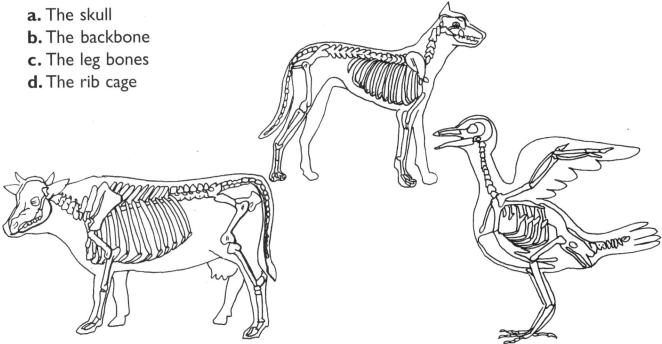

 **NOW**   Draw a picture of what the dog above would look like if it suddenly lost its skeleton.

Habitats

Most animals and plants can only live in certain environments. Humans, however, can live almost anywhere in the world using a variety of clothes, buildings and machines to enable them to live in their different environments. The habitat where a plant or animal lives (e.g. a pond, a tree, a wall) provides the organism with food, shelter and a safe place to reproduce.

Most organisms are best adapted to live in a certain habitat. For example:
1. A cactus (desert) – long roots to find water, fleshy stems to store water, thin needle-shaped leaves to stop water loss.
2. A squirrel (trees) – long claws for gripping, strong teeth for opening nuts, a bushy tail for balance.

Activity pages

Grouping Things Together
Learning objectives
- To know the differences between non-living and living things.
- To know the differences between plants and animals.
- To be able to group things according to their own criteria.

Discuss with the class the features of a set of similar objects (e.g. fruit). Ask them what these objects have in common (fruits can be eaten, they rot, have skin, grow on trees, etc.). Repeat this with sets of other objects (e.g. sports equipment, crockery, tools, etc.). Examples of sorting the pictures into two groups are: fly/do not fly; legs/no legs; wings/no wings; wheels/legs; move by sliding/do not move by sliding; plants/animals; living/not living; engine/no engine; leaves/no leaves; go on water/do not go on water. The children could be given the challenge of finding as many sets of two groups as possible.

What do Worms Like?
Learning objectives
- To be able to make a guess as to what conditions worms like to live in.
- To be able to design a fair experiment to test a guess.
- To be able to make observations and draw conclusions.

Discuss with the class where worms are usually found. What conditions do they think worms like: damp/dry, warm/cold, light/dark, smooth/rough, hard rock/soft soil. Explain to the class that they need to find out if worms prefer dark or light conditions. Show equipment that is available (e.g. soil, newspaper, measuring cylinders, water, active worms, trays and card). The children could cover half of a tray with a lid to make one side dark. Decide how many worms are to be placed in the tray. Where are the worms to be placed at the start? How long will they be left? What other things must be kept constant (e.g. temperature, dampness and type of soil). Discuss the importance of doing many trials to get an accurate result. Worms are best collected after heavy rain or pour water on to a grass area. Remember to return all animals collected to their original habitat.

Built to Survive
Learning objectives
- To know that animals have special features that help them live well in their habitat.

Show the class pictures of different environments (e.g. hot and sandy, cold and snowy). Ask, 'How would the animals that live in these places be different?'.

Oral work

Discuss how certain animals are adapted to survive in their habitats. What special features do the animals have? For example, fish are adapted for living in water: gills for breathing, fins for movement, colouring for camouflage. Woodlice are adapted for living under damp stones: flattened body, external skeleton to stop water loss.

Written work

The children could research and write about how worms help to improve the soil (i.e. help drainage, aerate soil, bury stones by lifting soil, add rotting leaves to soil). They could also look closely at worms and draw a labelled diagram with explanations (e.g. a worm's body is made up of segments that change in size to help it move, bristles on the underside of a worm help it to grip the soil, the worm's saddle is for reproduction).

ICT

Use CD-ROM and videos to show the habitat of an animal found locally (e.g. bird, small mammal, frog). How does the habitat provide shelter, food and protection for the animal?

Grouping Things Together

You will need

– Scissors

 **Key Idea**   There are differences between living and non-living things.

1. Cut out these pictures and then sort them into two groups. For example, 'the things in group one have legs' and 'the things in group two do not have legs'.

2. After you have done that, sort the pictures into two new groups.

What do Worms Like?

You will need
- Worms
- Soil
- Measuring cylinder
- Water
- Trays
- Newspaper
- Card

Key Idea — Worms prefer certain conditions in which to live.

● You are going to do an experiment to find out if worms prefer light or dark conditions. Write your plan and results below.

Title:

I want to find out if:

What I think will happen is:

To do my experiment, I:

In caring for the worms, I:

In my experiment I only changed one thing. I changed:

In my experiment I kept all the other things the same. The things that I kept the same were:

I found out that:

Built to Survive

Key Idea An animal has special body features that allow it to survive in its habitat. In its habitat, the animal needs to find food, reproduce and hide from other animals that want to eat it.

● Look at the two animals below and think about where they live and what they must be able to do to survive in their habitat.
Match the special features listed below to the animal.

Pointed head cuts through soil.	Webbed feet for swimming fast.	Brown skin to aid camouflage in soil.	Strong back legs for jumping.
Damp skin allows air to pass into blood.	Eyes positioned so can see but still hide.	Bristles to help movement.	Speckled skin to aid camouflage in the undergrowth.

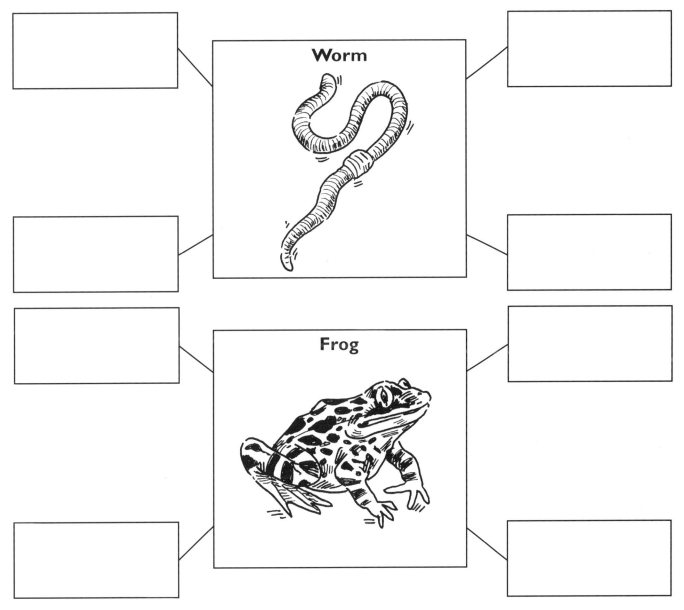

Temperature

A thermometer is usually used to measure temperature. A thermometer gives the temperature in degrees Celsius °C (sometimes called degrees Centigrade °C). There are many different types of thermometer, for example wall thermometers (scale -40°C to +50°C), dial thermometers and digital thermometers. Room and wall thermometers may also include the Fahrenheit scale. If the liquid gets segmented in the thermometer, place it in the freezer overnight.

Activity pages

Using a Thermometer
Learning objectives
- To be able to handle thermometers safely.
- To know that hands are inaccurate when measuring temperature.
- To know that thermometers are used to measure temperature.

When the right hand is placed in hot water then placed immediately in lukewarm water, the latter feels cold. When the left hand, however, is placed in cold water then placed immediately in lukewarm water, the latter feels hot. Our hands can only make comparative measures.

Remind the children not to handle the bulb end of the thermometer. Whatever the bulb touches, the thermometer tells how hot that object is. Ask them to read off the scale only when the liquid has stopped moving.

Safety – Test the hot water before the children put their hands in. Shorter thermometers (15cm) are safer to use than the long ones (30cm). Wrap some tape around the top end to prevent the thermometer rolling off the desk.

Everyday Temperatures
Learning objectives
- To know how to read a thermometer's scale.
- To know that thermometers can measure below 0°C.
- To know some everyday temperatures.
- To know that water boils at 100°C and freezes at 0°C.

The illustrations on the activity sheet should be placed as follows: boiling water – 100°C, fresh tea – 70°C, warm water – 50°C, hot day – 30°C, ice – 0°C, freezer – -10°C. Discuss other known temperatures. After completing the activity the children could construct a graph of the six temperatures to reinforce the idea of scales and negative numbers. They could also predict temperatures in different areas of the school, then measure them using thermometers.

How Thermometers Work
Learning objectives
- To know that the first thermometer was invented over 450 years ago.
- To understand that the present-day thermometer has developed from a number of ideas.
- To know that air and liquids take up more space when they get hot.

Set up the first two experiments on this sheet to show that air and liquids expand when they are warmed. Galileo invented the first Thermometer using this knowledge. The children should set up Galileo's sixteenth-century air thermometer at room temperature. In a warm place the air expands and pushes the liquid in the straw down. In a cool place the air contracts and pulls the liquid up the straw.

Oral work

Ask the children to describe what a thermometer is and what it is used for. In a thermometer, what is the little bulb at the bottom and why is the liquid coloured? Why are only some numbers shown on a thermometer's scale (why not all the numbers: 1,2,3 etc. to 100?). Children need to be confident in reading scales. Using a large demonstration thermometer will help them to practise reading a scale.

Written work

Ask the children to list the disadvantages of Galileo's early thermometer. Can they find out about other thermometers (e.g. bimetal – ovens, irons, car automatic choke; clinical). The children could research earlier thermometers. For example, Professor Celsius's (1701–1744) early thermometer scale (100°C = freezing point!!); Daniel Fahrenheit (1686–1736) and his scale (32°F = freezing and 212°F = boiling water).

ICT

Use a software package to construct graphs of temperature data. Use hand-held digital thermometers. Use an IT temperature sensor to present temperature readings on the computer screen. Use the Internet to find out about Galileo's water thermometer.

Using a Thermometer

You will need

- Beaker of hot water
- Beaker of lukewarm water
- Beaker of cold water
- Thermometer
- Ice

 **Key Idea** Thermometers are the only reliable way of testing how hot something is.

1. Place your right hand in the hot water and your left hand in the cold water. Then put your right hand in the lukewarm water. After feeling the hot water, what does the lukewarm water feel like?

2. Now place your left hand in the lukewarm water. After feeling the cold water, what does the lukewarm water feel like?

3. Do you think that using your hands is the best way of measuring temperature? Give a reason for you answer.

4. Using a thermometer, carefully measure each of the seven things below and record your results.

a. Your breath

b. Air

c. Under your arm

d. Your hand

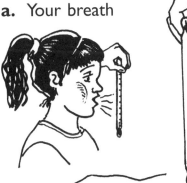

e. Ice

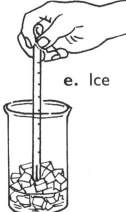

f. Water from the cold tap

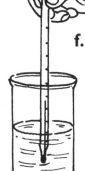

g. Water from the hot tap

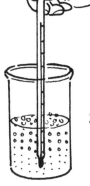

Everyday Temperatures

You will need
– Scissors
– Glue

Key Idea

There are some everyday temperatures that are easily recognisable.

Cut out the pictures and glue them on to the correct squares.

Warm water

Fresh tea

Freezer

Boiling water

Ice

Hot day

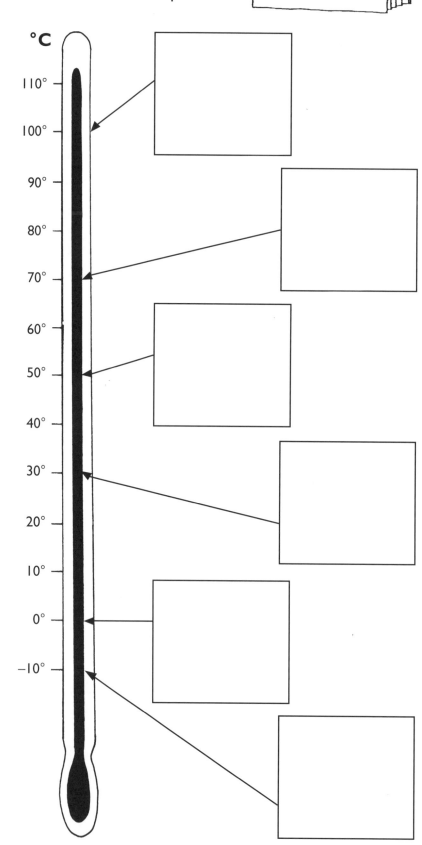

°C
110°
100°
90°
80°
70°
60°
50°
40°
30°
20°
10°
0°
−10°

How Thermometers Work

 **Key Idea**

Thermometers have developed from the idea that liquid expands when heated and contracts when cooled.

You will need
- Screw-top plastic bottle
- Straw
- Beaker of water
- Coffee powder

● The first thermometers used air to show how warm or cold an object was. Later, liquid thermometers were invented. Today, classroom thermometers contain a liquid that gets bigger (expands) when heated and gets smaller (contracts) when cooled.

1. **Air needs more space when heated.**
   Look at the experiment below. What do you think will happen to the balloon if the bottle is placed in the fridge?

Air

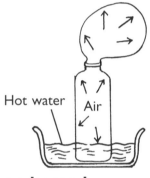

Hot water Air

Fridge

2. **Liquids need more space when heated.**
   a. Look at the experiment below. What do you think will happen to the liquid in the straw when the bottle is put into hot water?
   b. What do you think will happen to the water in the straw when the bottle is put into ice?

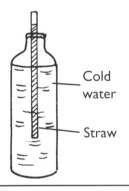

Cold water

Straw

Hot water

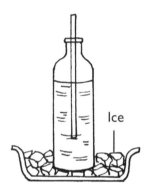

Ice

3. a. Set up your own version of Galileo's sixteenth-century air thermometer as shown.
   b. Place warm hands around the plastic bottle. Do not squeeze the bottle. What happens?
   c. Place your thermometer in a cool place. What happens?

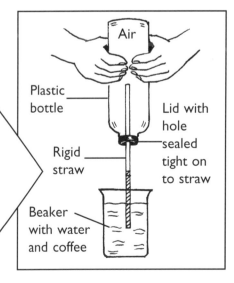

Air

Plastic bottle

Rigid straw

Lid with hole sealed tight on to straw

Beaker with water and coffee

Keeping Cool – Keeping Warm

Animals that live in very hot places have developed special features to keep cool, and animals that live in cold environments have special features to keep warm. Protection against the cold includes thick fur, fat layer, short ears and nose, hibernation, migration, shivering, huddling. 'Huddling' is a term used to describe animals grouping together to keep warm. Those in the middle of the group keep warmer than those on the outside. The group is constantly shifting so that all members of the group have a turn on the outside. Protection against the heat includes sweating, panting, being nocturnal, living underground, thin fur, long nose, large ears. Large ears have a large surface area to lose heat in the air. Blood vessels in the ear carry warm blood and the heat is passed into the air.

Safety – The children should be carefully supervised when using jars, thermometers and hot water. Any spillages should be cleaned up immediately.

Activity pages

Keeping Warm – Emperor Penguins
Learning objectives
- To put forward an idea that can be tested in the classroom.
- To be able to carry out a fair test by changing one thing.
- To make observations and record measurements.

Ask the children to put forward ideas as to how 'huddling behaviour' could be tested in the classroom. Discuss how the experiment is to be made a fair test. Use equal quantities of hot water in the jars, same number of jars, equal intervals between measurements. Note that doing the experiment in a cool room will bring the temperature down more quickly. Best results are achieved if the thermometer is not moved up and down in the water. Provide each group of children with one jar lid with a hole in it.

Keeping Cool – Large Ears or Small Ears
Learning objectives
- To make a prediction as to what will happen in an experiment.
- To be able to design a fair test.
- To be able to draw conclusions from results.

Put forward the problem of how to find out which size of animal ear loses most body heat. Show the class the apparatus that is available for them to do the experiment. Use two different-sized foil trays from the supermarket to represent ears. Are both trays to be tested simultaneously or will one tray be tested first, then the other afterwards (suggest measurement intervals of five to ten minutes)?

Keeping Cool – Sweating
Learning objectives
- To make observations and record measurements.
- To compare findings to an initial guess.

Discuss with the children why they feel cold after getting out of a swimming pool. (The water is evaporating from the skin's surface and the body is losing heat to carry out this evaporation.) The prediction is that the wet container will lose heat more quickly than the dry one. Discuss how to make the experiment a fair test. Use equal-sized jars, equal amounts of water in each jar, similar starting temperatures, equal layers of kitchen roll on each jar. (Using hot water on the kitchen paper would be fairer. Do not allow the skin to dry out.)

Oral work

Discuss the ideas that mammals are able to control their body temperature and that animals have developed adaptations to be able to live in extreme environments. (Note that the body's chemistry operates at an optimum temperature; too hot or too cold and the body organs cease to function. Animals have different optimum body temperatures.) Discuss what happens when we get cold (shivering – muscles working to create heat; goose pimples – hairs erect to trap air; blood vessels near the skin's surface close down). Discuss what happens when we get hot (sweating, red-faced – blood vessels dilate to allow greater blood flow and get rid of excess heat).

Written work

The children could explain how the human body controls its temperature, find the coldest and hottest places in the world and find out the body temperature of different mammals.

ICT

The children could enter their results into a data-handling package and produce simple bar charts.

Keeping Warm – Emperor Penguins

Key Idea — Emperor penguins keep warm by huddling together.

You will need
- Six jars with lids (one with a hole)
- Thermometer
- Measuring cylinder
- Stopwatch
- Hot water

1. Arrange five jars (penguins) around one central jar.
   Add an equal amount of hot water to each jar and replace the lids.
   Place the thermometer in the central jar through a hole in the lid.
   Take the temperature of the central jar every two minutes until you have ten readings.
   (Remember not to remove the thermometer from the jar.)
   Write your results in the column headed 'Huddled penguin' in the table below.

	Huddled penguin	Separated penguin
Temperature at 2 minutes	°C	°C
Temperature at 4 minutes	°C	°C
Temperature at 6 minutes	°C	°C
Temperature at 8 minutes	°C	°C
Temperature at 10 minutes	°C	°C
Temperature at 12 minutes	°C	°C
Temperature at 14 minutes	°C	°C
Temperature at 16 minutes	°C	°C
Temperature at 18 minutes	°C	°C
Temperature at 20 minutes	°C	°C

2. Do the experiment again, but this time keep the six penguins (jars) separate.
   Take the temperature of the middle jar every two minutes until you have ten readings.
   Write your results in the column headed 'Separated penguin'.

3. Which penguin cooled the least?

4. a. Which penguin cooled the most?
   b. Why do you think this was?

 **NOW** — Explain how huddling helps to keep penguins warm.

Keeping Cool – Large Ears or Small Ears

 **Key Idea**

The size of an animal's ears is related to how much heat the animal loses.

You will need
- Large foil dishes
- Small foil dishes
- Measuring cylinder
- Stopwatch
- Thermometer
- Hot water

● You are going to do an experiment to find out whether small or large ears are better at keeping an animal cool.
Write your plan and results below.

Title:

I want to find out if:

What I think will happen is:

To do my experiment, I:

For safety reasons, I:

To make this a fair experiment, I:

My results table. (Complete your table on the back of this sheet.)

Time	Large dish	Small dish
	°C	°C
	°C	°C
	°C	°C

I found out that:

© Belair (copiable page)

Keeping Cool – Sweating

You will need
- Two jars
- Two thermometers
- Kitchen roll
- Measuring cylinder
- Elastic bands
- Hot water

 **Key Idea**   Sweating helps the body lose heat.

1. Wrap both jars in equal amounts of kitchen roll (skin) and secure with rubber bands.
   Add equal amounts of hot water to each jar.
   It is important to keep one skin dry.
   Wet the other skin with hot water.
   Take the temperature of each jar every two minutes until you have ten readings.

   Record your results in the table below.

	Wet skin	Dry skin
Temperature at 2 minutes	°C	°C
Temperature at 4 minutes	°C	°C
Temperature at 6 minutes	°C	°C
Temperature at 8 minutes	°C	°C
Temperature at 10 minutes	°C	°C
Temperature at 12 minutes	°C	°C
Temperature at 14 minutes	°C	°C
Temperature at 16 minutes	°C	°C
Temperature at 18 minutes	°C	°C
Temperature at 20 minutes	°C	°C

2. After 20 minutes, which jar has cooled the most?

3. Does the wet skin help the jar to lose or retain heat? How?

4. Show your results as a graph.

 **NOW**   Explain three things you did to make this a fair experiment.

Solids and Liquids

It can be confusing to group substances as either 'liquid' or 'solid'. Think of grouping them as in a Venn diagram (e.g. shaving foam could fit into the overlapping area of 'solid–liquid'). The important thing is to find out the children's reasons for their classification. Choose carefully the substances the children are asked to sort, observe and describe.

Solids have a definite shape and do not change. They are often strong and can be tested to see if they bend, stretch, tear or break. Liquids take the shape of their container, they can be poured and you can generally put your hand into them.

Activity pages

Describing Solids and Liquids
Learning objectives
● To be able to identify a solid or a liquid.
● To know that some solids can behave like liquids.
● To know that liquids can pour and take the shape of their container.

Introduce the activity by describing to the class an object hidden behind a screen. Describe the object's properties but not what it does. This will help to revise language skills in describing properties of materials (e.g. shape, size, colour, texture, strength).

For this activity sheet, choose a range of solids (hard, bendy, stretchy, easily melted, powder or grain). Include solids that pour (e.g. sand, salt, iron filings, powders) and solids that stretch or squash (e.g. a balloon, a rubber band, cotton wool). Choose liquids with a range of runniness and colour, (e.g. coffee, milk, baby oil, PVA glue, liquid soap, syrups). Some substances can lead to good discussion about what makes a solid a solid and a liquid a liquid. Pouring could be tested by placing the substances in jars with lids and tipping them at different angles. Ask whether the substance takes the shape of the jar.

Safety – Care is needed not to get liquids into eyes or cuts. Care is also needed when testing solids for properties.

Mixing Solids and Liquids
Learning objectives
● To know how to measure accurately in millilitres.
● To know that when salt dissolves in water it cannot be seen but does remain in the water.

When 50ml of salt is added to 100ml of dried peas, the new total is not 150ml. The salt particles hide in the gaps between the peas. When 50ml of salt is added to 100ml of water, the same happens. When dissolved, the salt particles spread out and hide among the water particles.

Changing Water
Learning objectives
● To know that ice is a solid that forms when water freezes.
● To know that ice melts into a liquid when warmed.
● To know that some solids need to be heated to make them melt.

Oral work

Discuss solid powders and pastes and those overlapping areas between liquids and solids. The rain cycle could be discussed to introduce the terms 'evaporation' and 'condensation'.

Written work

The children could also investigate and record (using graphs) the melting points of different substances (all pure substances have a set melting point).

ICT

Use CD-ROM software to investigate: temperatures at which substances melt or boil, molten rock and conditions and temperatures in polar regions of the world.

Discuss the differences between solids and liquids. Show the class some ice and ask 'Why is it a solid?', 'What would happen to it if left in a warm room?'. Ask the class how they would measure how fast an ice cube melts. Would they take measurements every five minutes of the height/length/weight/area of puddle? Ask the class for examples of other solids that can be melted easily (e.g. butter, chocolate). This activity sheet introduces the idea of evaporating water. Discuss what would happen to the liquid once the ice has melted (dries up – evaporates).

Describing Solids and Liquids

You will need
− Some named substances
− Stiff card

Key Idea Liquids and solids have different properties.

● Test whether each substance can be poured, scratched, bent, stretched, reshaped or seen through. Write the substance name in column 1 and tick the appropriate boxes.

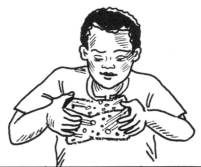

Substance	It can be poured	It is hard (can be scratched)	It is bendy	It is see-through	It has a definite/ fixed shape	It is stretchy

 **NOW** Write down which substances are solids and which are liquids.

© Belair (copiable page)

Mixing Solids and Liquids

You will need
- Two beakers
- Measuring cylinder
- 100ml salt
- 50ml peas
- 100ml water

Key Idea
When liquids, solids, or liquids and solids are mixed together, the total volume is often not equal to the two original volumes added together.

1. Add 50ml of salt to 100ml of peas in a beaker.

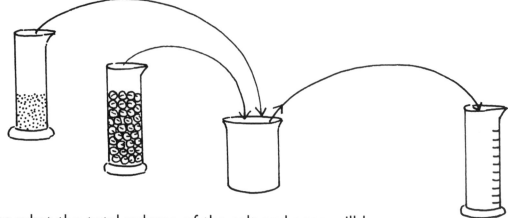

2. a. Guess what the total volume of the salt and peas will be.
   b. Find out if you are correct.
   c. Explain what has happened and try to suggest a reason why this might have happened.

3. Add 50ml of salt to 100ml of water in a beaker.

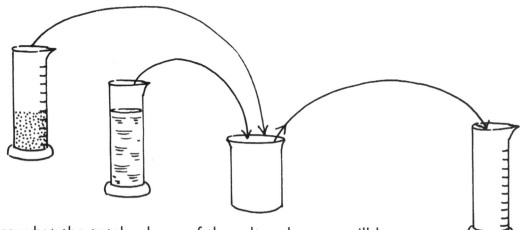

4. a. Guess what the total volume of the salt and water will be.
   b. Find out if you are correct.
   c. Explain what you have found out and suggest a reason why this might have happened.

 **NOW**

Look at the picture opposite. The salt particles hide in-between the peas. When you mix 50ml of salt and 100ml of water, why can you not see the salt particles?

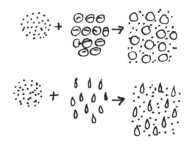

BELAIR ACTIVE SCIENCE 4   © Belair (copiable page)

Changing Water

You will need
– Scissors

Key Idea Water can undergo changes from liquid to solid and from liquid to gas.

● Cut out the eight words and pictures at the bottom of the page and stick them on to the chart.

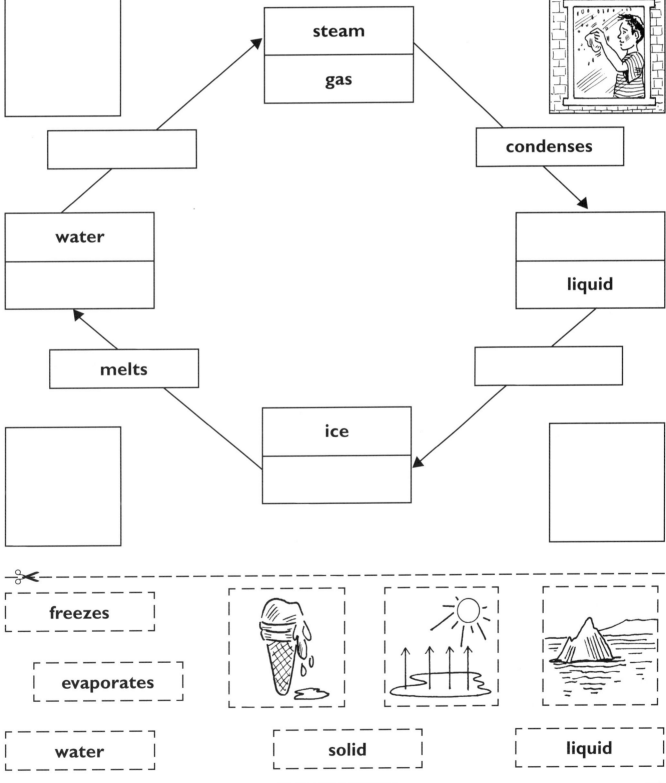

steam

gas

condenses

water

liquid

melts

ice

---

freezes

evaporates

water

solid

liquid

Separating Materials

Materials that are mixed together can be separated in a number of ways. They can be sieved. Filter paper is a fine sieve made from interlocking fibres, packed closely together. Filter papers used in schools can be bought in different grades according to their ability to separate solids suspended in liquids. Solids that have been dissolved in water (e.g. salt) can be separated from the water by leaving the water to evaporate (dry up). Distilling is a way of separating solids from a liquid by capturing the evaporated liquid. Decanting was used by the Ancient

Egyptians. Water was collected from the Nile in large jars. These would be left to stand to allow the mud to settle at the bottom of the jar. Tipping the jar carefully allowed the solid and water to be separated. Chromatography is a method of separating a mixture of coloured inks. Add a black felt tip mark to a paper towel. Slowly add drops of water to the spot. As the water travels through the paper, different colours will appear – they have been separated.

Safety – Do not pour any solids down the sink.

Activity pages

Separating Mixtures
Learning objectives
- To know that there are a variety of ways to separate mixtures.

When doing the first activity you could add some brass screws to the activity to show that the magnet cannot separate all metals from wood shavings. Wood shavings are obtainable from pet shops. The paper teabag acts as a filter to separate the tea leaves from the water. It allows the dissolved flavouring to pass through the filter, but the larger tea leaves to remain in the bag. As an extension to this experiment the children could find out how the Ancient Egyptians obtained clean water from the Nile.

Adding Substances to Water
Learning objectives
- To know that some solids disappear in water.
- To know that some solids do not change when added to water.
- To know that some solids break down and disappear but leave a colour behind in the water.
- To make predictions.

The activity works best if warm water is used, if only small quantities of substances are added to the water and if substances are stirred with the water. If a colour change occurs in the water, but the solids have disappeared, then the substance has dissolved. Note that dissolved substances are still there in the water but have disappeared from sight. Prior to doing this activity sheet, build up a word bank, for example, colours, textures (powdery, lumpy, smooth, gritty), sink, float, shiny.

Separating Substances by Filtering
Learning objectives
- To know that a filter will separate some solids from water.
- To know that a filter cannot separate dissolved substances from water.

In this activity the filter paper acts like a tea bag. The mud is held back by the filter paper rather like tea leaves in a tea bag. When cleaning salty water the salt is able to pass through the filter paper just like the flavour passes out of a tea bag. The filter paper has tiny holes and certain things will pass through (i.e. dissolved substances). When doing this activity remind children not to: 1. Overfill the filter paper cone or else the mixture will travel down the outside of the filter and into the beaker, and 2. Poke the inside of the filter in order to speed up the filtering process as it will split open. How will the children know if the filter has successfully removed the salt from the mixture? You could evaporate the filtrate: remove the water and leave behind the salt solids. Do this overnight or heat the filtrate over a candle flame.

Oral work

- Show the class various examples of filters found in the home (e.g. coffee filter, sieve, colander, air filter, DIY facemask filter).
- Discuss the children's experience of adding solids to liquids (e.g. sugar to tea, coffee to water, making custard, gravy or hot chocolate).

Written work

The children could find out how water is treated after leaving our homes and factories. Sediment tanks allow solids to settle. (Link this to Ancient Egyptians' siphoning Nile water from jars). The children could also shake up some soil in a tall jar, leave this to settle overnight and then look at the layers formed.

Separating Mixtures

You will need

- Magnet
- Dish
- Beakers
- Nails
- Wood shavings
- Rice
- Old tights or pop sock
- Water
- Tea bag
- Spoon

Key Idea There are a variety of ways to separate mixtures of substances.

1. Carry out the three experiments shown in the pictures and then answer the questions below.

a.

Nails

Wood shavings

b.

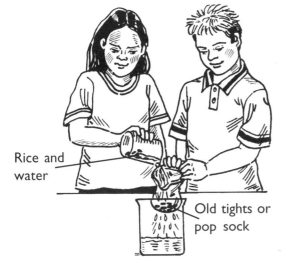

Rice and water

Old tights or pop sock

c.

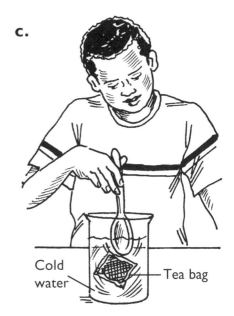

Cold water

Tea bag

2. What can you use to separate metal nails from water?

3. How did the tights separate the rice from the water?

4. Using equipment found in the kitchen, how could you separate marbles from water? Draw a diagram.

5. a. Explain what happened when you placed your tea bag in the water.
   b. How does a tea bag work?

 **NOW** If you had a mixture of sand and water, which method would you use to separate them?

Adding Substances to Water

 **Key Idea** Some substances will change when added to water while others will not.

You will need
- Nine beakers of warm water
- Substances listed in the table
- Tablespoons

1. Look at each of your substances and fill in the first two empty columns in the table below.

2. Take a tablespoon of each substance and add each to separate beakers of water. Complete the table below.

Substance tested	What my substance looks like	What I think will happen to the substance when mixed with water	What did happen to the substance when mixed with water	Did my substance dissolve?
Brown sugar				
Bath salts				
Iron filings				
Instant coffee				
Soap powder				
White sugar				
Pasta shapes				
Soda crystals				
Salt				

Separating Substances by Filtering

You will need
- Two pieces of filter paper
- Funnel
- Two beakers
- Muddy water
- Salty water

Key Idea   Dirty water can be cleaned by filtering it.

1. Make a filter to clean dirty water.

Fold your filter paper in half.

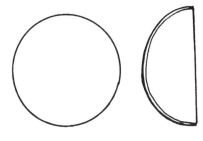   Open it up into a cone.

Fold it in half again.

Place it in a funnel.

2. Pour the muddy water slowly into the filter paper.
   Do not pour the muddy water over the top of the paper.
   Watch what filters through.
   Keep pouring more muddy water into the filter paper.

3. What filters through into the clean beaker?

4. What is left behind on the filter paper?

5. Do you think that the water in the beaker
   is clean enough to drink? Why?

6. Now set up an experiment to filter salty
   water. Set up your experiment using clean
   equipment and new filter paper.

7. Pour the salty water slowly into the clean
   filter paper. Watch what filters through into
   the beaker. Keep adding more salty water
   into the filter paper.

8. What has filtered through into the clean beaker?
9. What is left behind on the filter paper?

 **NOW**   How do you know whether the water that has passed through
the filter has any salt in it?

Changing Materials

This chapter looks at more demanding investigations suitable for children who have completed the chapter on 'Separating Materials'. Each activity is started by posing a problem. Brainstorm ideas with the children. Ask them to suggest things that could be changed in the experiments.

Activity pages

What's Wrong With My Experiment?
Learning objectives
- To be able to criticise an unfair test and suggest alternatives.
- To be able to put forward ideas.

Tell the class that you are going to do this experiment. You want them to look carefully at the equipment that you use and the way that you do the experiment. They must decide if it is a fair experiment. When doing the experiment, exaggerate the differences: many white sugar lumps, few white sugar granules; large spoon for stirring slowly, small spoon for stirring very fast; use a small amount of cold water in the small beaker and a large amount of hot water from the kettle in the large beaker. When you have done the experiment ask the children which sugar dissolved first – granules or lumps. Ask them if they can say why the granules or the lumps dissolve more quickly. The granules should dissolve more quickly, but it could be due to lots of different reasons (e.g. water temperature, size of beaker, amount of water, amount of sugar used, speed of stirring, size of spoon). You can do this as a speed test and see which dissolves first or do one at a time and time each experiment.

Dissolving Sugar
Learning objectives
- To be able to design a fair test.
- To be able to choose apparatus for an experiment.
- To be able to make and record observations and measurements.

Before handing out the activity sheet, ask the children to brainstorm the equipment that they might need to do the experiment (e.g. beakers, sugar, spoons, measuring cylinder, water, timer) and the things that need to be the same for each experiment to make it a fair test (e.g. same amounts of water, same temperature of water, same spoon size, same amounts of sugar, same speed of stirring, same-sized beakers). Ask the children how they would make sure that the amount of granules and cube are the same (e.g. take two cubes – crush one to make granules and use one as a lump). The two tests do not have to be done at the same time. The experiments can be repeated to increase the result's validity or you can combine the class results.

The Evaporation Race
Learning objectives
- To know that the speed of evaporation depends on warmth, wind and surface area.
- To be able to draw conclusions from results.

This experiment could be completed in class, but containers will probably have to be adapted according to what is available. Brainstorm with the children how they would make this a fair test (e.g. keep containers in the same area in the room, put equal amounts of water in each container, start with water the same temperature). Ask the children to predict what will happen. The narrow-necked containers should lose water slowly and the wide-open containers should lose water more quickly.

Oral work

Refresh the children's knowledge of evaporation and dissolving. Link rate of evaporation to everyday experiences, such as towels spread out to dry, damp clothes left in kit bags, pavements drying quickly on a hot day.

Written work

The children could design experiments that investigate dissolving brown sugar cubes versus dissolving white sugar cubes, dissolving salt in hot water versus dissolving salt in cold water, dampened cloths drying in different areas, drying cloths of different materials or drying scrunched up materials versus drying spread out materials.

ICT

Use CD-ROM software to investigate dissolving and evaporation. Produce bar charts for 'The Evaporating Race' activity sheet showing the levels of water remaining over time.

What's Wrong With My Experiment?

Key Idea — An experiment should be a fair test if the results are to be reliable.

● Some children wanted to find out if white sugar cubes dissolve quicker in water than sugar granules. This is their experiment. It certainly is not a fair test. Can you spot six mistakes in their experiment? Explain how you would correct each fault to make it a fair test. The first one has been done for you.

Sugar granules

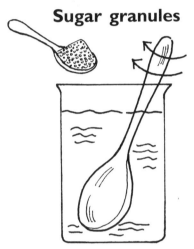

Sugar cubes

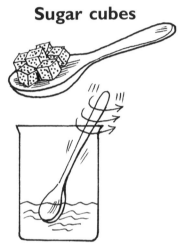

Mistake	Correction
1. One spoon is stirring fast and one is stirring slowly.	1. Stir both spoons at the same speed.
2.	
3.	
4.	
5.	
6.	

Dissolving Sugar

Key Idea | A fair test is needed in order to judge whether brown sugar dissolves more quickly than white sugar.

You will need
- Measuring cylinder
- Brown and white sugar
- Spoons
- Beakers
- Water
- Stopwatch

● You are going to do an experiment to find out if brown sugar dissolves quicker than white sugar. Write your plan and results below.

Title:

I want to find out if:

What I think will happen is:

To do my experiment, I:

For safety reasons, I:

To make this a fair experiment, I:

My results table.

Experiment 1	Brown sugar	White sugar
Time taken to dissolve		

Experiment 2	Brown sugar	White sugar
Time taken to dissolve		

I found out that:

The Evaporation Race

Key Idea

The speed of evaporation depends on warmth, wind and surface area.

1. Imagine that you are going to conduct an experiment to find out which of the containers below would lose water most quickly. Complete the sentences below.

   a. We put (the same/different) _____ amounts of water into each container.

   b. I think container number _____ will lose most water because _____

   _____

   c. I think container number _____ will lose least water because _____

   _____

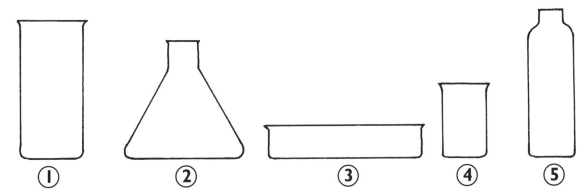

①   ②   ③   ④   ⑤

2. Draw a line on each container to show where you think the level of the water will be after five days at room temperature.

3. Join these words to the correct picture.

   These clothes dry fast   **These clothes dry slowly**   **Warm**

   Windy   **Cloudy**   **Sunny**   **No wind**

Background

When two objects rub together, friction occurs. If there is a lot of friction between surfaces, they grip well. If there is very little friction, the surfaces slip over each other. Whenever friction occurs a number of things happen: the objects get hot, they begin to wear out and they slow down. Friction can be a problem but it can also be useful. Air resistance is a type of friction. Air rubs against a car and slows it down and wastes fuel, but parachutists rely on air resistance to slow their descent. Some materials create more friction than others. For example, rubber causes a lot of friction between objects. Metals are smooth and shiny and there is little friction between the surfaces. However, rust on a metal surface increases friction. Oil and grease helps reduce friction.

Activity pages

Paper Helicopters

Learning objectives
- To be able to record observations in sentences or pictures.
- To know that air resistance is a force that slows objects.

Demonstrate how the paper helicopter is made and how to drop it. A word bank might be useful (e.g. 'twirl', 'twist', 'spin', 'swoop', 'glide', 'drop', 'fast', 'slow', 'curl', 'swerve', 'turn'). Encourage the children to observe whether the helicopter turns in the same direction each time it is dropped and whether it falls at the same speed.

Safety – Do not allow children to climb on to chairs and desks to release their helicopters. It is sufficient to release the helicopters at hand-held height.

Slippery Shoes

Learning objectives
- To be able to design a fair test.
- To make and record careful measurements.
- To know that repeating an experiment helps to make the answer more reliable.
- To know that the force between two moving surfaces in contact is called friction.

Before handing out the activity sheet, show the class several different shoes (e.g. wellington boot, slipper, trainer, high-heeled shoe) and explain that you want to find out which shoe gives the best grip on the table surface. Discuss the variables (e.g. shoe size, weight, surface area of sole, material shoe is made of, design of sole tread). Ask how a fair experiment can be designed (e.g. using standard weights or marbles of the same size, placing the weights in the pot not throwing them in, moving the shoes over equal distances (e.g.15cm). A forcemeter could be used instead of the listed equipment.

Friction on a Bicycle

Learning objectives
- To know that friction can be both a disadvantage and an advantage.
- To know that some materials increase friction.
- To know that oil reduces friction.
- To know that friction causes objects to wear down, slow down and get hot.

Discussion could include why different parts of a bicycle are made from different materials. Discuss why it is important that a bicycle's wheels grip the ground and ask how this grip is increased (i.e. tread on the tyres). Where else on the bike is friction a good thing (e.g. handle bar grips, saddle, brake blocks)? Friction can also be a disadvantage. Ask the children what is used to reduce friction between the moving metal parts (e.g. the wheel chain and cogs (oil)).

Oral work

Introduce the idea of friction by discussing why a moving object would eventually slow down and come to a halt. Explain friction as a force that tries to stop one object sliding over the other. Discuss evidence of the actions of friction (e.g. wear on shoes, tyres, bicycle brake blocks). Discuss why friction can be a bad thing (e.g. causes wear, heat and slows things down) and why friction can be a good thing (e.g. allows objects to grip, slows down moving objects, such as parachutes).

Written work

Ask the children to explain the advantages and disadvantages of air resistance.

ICT

The children could use a software package that allows them to enter their data from the experiment 'Slippery Shoes' to create a bar chart.

Paper Helicopters

You will need
- Sheet of A4 paper
- Ruler
- Scissors
- Paperclips

 **Key Idea** Air resistance slows down a moving object.

1. Use the template below to make a paper helicopter.

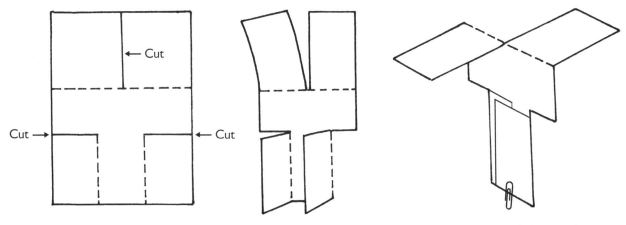

2. Following each of the diagrams below, test how each of the designs falls to the ground.

Helicopter design	How the helicopter fell to the ground

Slippery Shoes

Key Idea

There is some friction between the sole of a shoe and the surface with which it has contact.

You will need

– Eight to ten different types of shoe
– Table
– Ruler
– String
– Container
– Weights
– Hook

1. Set up the experiment as shown in the diagram below and find out how much weight is needed to move each of your shoes the length of the ruler. Draw each of your shoes in the boxes below and write under each, the weight needed. If you have time, test each shoe twice.

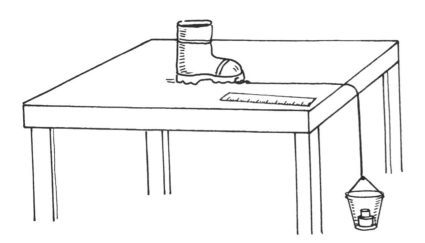

2. Which shoe has the most friction with the table?

3. Which shoe has the least friction with the table?

4. Name the force pulling the container of weights downwards.

a.	b.	c.	d.	e.
f.	g.	h.	i.	j.

 **NOW**

Why do you think some shoes are better than others at gripping the table surface?

Friction on a Bicycle

Key Idea

Friction on a bicycle can be both an advantage and a disadvantage.

1. Complete the following table.

Bicycle part	Material bicycle part is made from	Is friction an advantage or a disadvantage?
Saddle		
Handle bar grip		
Tyre		
Pedal		
Chain		
Pump		
Frame		
Bell		
Mirror		

2. Look at the two illustrations below. Make a list of how the illustration on the right differs from the one on the left. Give a reason for each difference.

Background

In looking at friction as a type of force, the children are asked to design their own experiments to test out ideas. The ideas are related to friction, including air and water resistance, as a force that slows moving objects. The activity sheets are to be used as a guide. Suitable headings form a structure enabling the child to put forward ideas, plan an experiment and then carry out a fair test.

Activity pages

Water Resistance

Learning objectives
- To suggest which shape will move most easily.
- To design an experiment to test an idea.
- To design a fair test.
- To record findings in a table or a chart.
- To make conclusions from results.

The children need to understand the importance of fair testing. They should use the same amount of plasticine for each shape tested, test each shape more than once, start timing and stop timing the plasticine shape in the same places and place each shape in the water equally (no pushing down).

Sliding Margarine Tub

Learning objectives
- To suggest which material will create the most friction.
- To design a fair test.
- To record findings in a table or a chart.
- To make conclusions from results.
- To carry out an experiment safely.

Materials to be investigated could include: carpet, wallpaper, tin foil, wood, towelling, carpet underlay, floor tiles. Two methods of doing this activity are: 1. Placing the tub on a material on the board and lifting the board, measuring the height at which the tub slides down, and 2. Measuring the weight needed to drag the tub over the material.

Floor Crawler

Learning objectives
- To know that the force of the elastic band turns the toy.
- To know that more turns make the toy travel further.
- To know that the metal washer reduces friction because it is smooth.
- To know that the elastic bands around the can increase friction.

Show a floor crawler in operation. Ask how it works. It moves because the elastic band that is twisted around the stick unwinds. Because the stick is dragging on the floor, the can moves. Ask why the can has elastic bands around it (i.e. for better grip). What happens if they are removed? Why is the wood block used (i.e. lifts long stick off the edge of the can and stops it rubbing)? Why is a metal washer used? How does friction help and hinder this toy (i.e. needs to grip floor but moving parts need to spin freely)?

Safety – Tape the long wire hook at the end to prevent any poking incidents. Make the holes in the tin cans yourself.

Oral work

Explain how the activity sheets guide the children through the process of carrying out their own investigation. Discuss what it is that they are trying to find out in their experiments. Remind them that in carrying out the experiments they will change only one factor and keep the other factors the same. For example, why would it be confusing to use plasticine shapes that are different in amount? Discuss safety issues.

Written work

Ask the children to draw conclusions from their results and observations. For example, if the plasticine cube is the slowest, why is this? Or why could the tub be lifted higher before sliding when using carpet underlay? The children could also write a set of instructions for, 'How to Build a Floor Crawler'.

ICT

The children could research information about streamlining in water animals (e.g. seals, fish), boats, sports (e.g. swimmers, cyclists) and cars. They could also research where water resistance is a good thing.

Water Resistance

Key Idea Streamlined objects move more freely through water.

You will need
- Tall plastic drink bottle
- Five equal amounts of plasticine
- Water
- Stopwatch

● Do an experiment to find out what shape moves through water most easily. First mould your five pieces of plasticine into a cube, a cone, a cylinder, a ball and a sausage shape. Write your plan and results below.

Title:

I want to find out if:

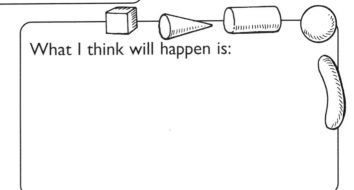

What I think will happen is:

To do my experiment, I:

For safety reasons, I:

To make this a fair experiment, I:

My results table. (Complete your table on the back of this sheet.)

Shape	1 Time taken	2 Time taken

I found out that:

Sliding Margarine Tub

You will need
- Ruler
- String
- Board
- Weights
- Margarine tub
- Various materials

Key Idea Different materials create different amounts of friction.

- You are going to do an experiment to find out which material gives the most grip (friction) with the margarine tub.

Title:

I want to find out if:

What I think will happen is:

To do my experiment, I:

For safety reasons, I:

To make this a fair experiment, I:

My results table. (Complete your table on the back of this sheet.)

Material tested	Amount of weight

I found out that:

Floor Crawler

Key Idea A floor crawler uses friction to its advantage, but also to its disadvantage.

You will need
- Tin can
- Elastic bands
- Match
- Wire hook
- Wooden square block with a hole through the centre
- Sticky tape
- Metal washer
- Wooden stick

1. Put these words on to the diagram of the floor crawler below.

Tin can   Wooden block   Metal washer
Wooden stick   Elastic band

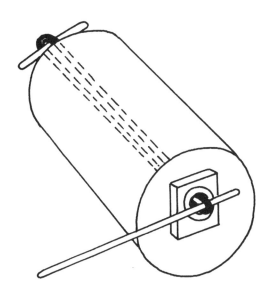

2. Make your own floor crawler by following the diagrams below.

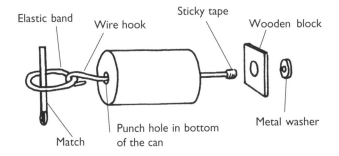

Elastic band   Wire hook   Sticky tape   Wooden block

Match   Punch hole in bottom of the can   Metal washer

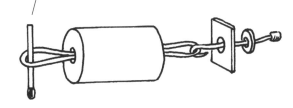

Match stops rubber band going into can.

3. Fill in the gaps below.

a. The _____ reduces friction between the wooden stick and the wooden block.

b. The _____ prevents the long stick from rubbing on the tin can.

c. Elastic bands can be wrapped around the tin can to create _____ and prevent the tin can from _____ .

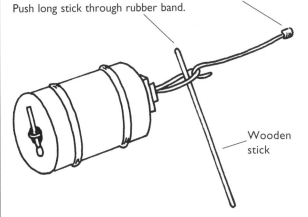

Push long stick through rubber band.

Wire hook can finally be removed.

Wooden stick

Electricity

For electricity to flow through a wire you need energy. The simplest way to provide this energy is by using a cell, often called a battery (though a battery means a collection of cells joined together). Chemicals in the cell push the electricity around the wire. This push is measured in volts. Different cells have different voltages shown by a number on the cell (e.g. 1.5V or 9V). The bigger the voltage the bigger the energy supply. For electricity to flow there must be a complete circuit – a path from one end of the cell to the other. The first battery was invented in 1800 by Volta. He discovered that two metals (silver and zinc) could work with a liquid (a brine solution) to make electricity.

Activity pages

Conductors and Insulators
Learning objectives
- To know that materials that let electricity pass through them are conductors.
- To know that materials that do not let electricity pass through them are insulators.

Show the children a light bulb and ask them how they would get this to light up in the classroom. They would need wire, battery, holders for the battery and bulb. Introduce the word 'cell' as the correct term. Build the circuit with the class and explain the correct procedure for putting the cells into the holder and joining the wires to the bulb holder. If the bulb does not light check if the cells are the correct way round, if the bulb is screwed in tightly, if the bulb is broken, if the cells are 'dead' and if the metal wires are twisted tightly on to the bulb holder. Use glass, marble, coins, bottle tops, nails, screws, foil, paper, card, wood, plant material, stone, plastic.

Looking at Batteries
Learning objectives
- To know that a battery's power is measured in volts.
- To know the difference between a cell and a battery.
- To know that the ends of a battery are marked as + and -.

Bulbs are made to match certain voltages. A 1.5V bulb works well when connected to a new 1.5V cell (or two slightly used ones). In this activity, use a 4.5V bulb. The 9V cell will damage a 1.5V bulb. In connecting the bulb to different cells, the children will begin to appreciate that more volts provide a brighter light (more electrical energy). Modern batteries are similar to Volta's first battery: zinc and carbon (like pencil lead) with a chemical paste. You could show the class a 1.5V cell cut in half. Take a 4.5V battery, peel the outer paper off; this reveals three 1.5V cells.

Switches
Learning objectives
- To construct a switch.
- To explain how switches work.

Switches work by closing and opening a gap in a circuit. There are many types of switches: press, sliding, rocker, tilt, magnetic, dimmer (variable). The pencil dimmer switch works like a variable resistor – the closer the wires are together the brighter the bulb becomes.

Oral work

Discuss what batteries are used for, where you find them being used and why they come in different sizes.

How do you know how powerful a battery is? What information is shown on it?

Discuss why a torch may not be working (e.g. batteries – dead, missing or wrong way; bulb – broken, missing or not screwed in tightly; switch – broken).

Written work

The children could do a survey of the different switches found in the home (e.g. press – calculator, remote, microwave; rocker – light switches; dimmer – radio volume, light, cooker; pull cord).

Ask them to research Thomas Edison – inventor of the electric light bulb in 1879.

ICT

Introduce computer-controlled technology (i.e. use a simple computer language to control sensors to operate models). This requires a computer, sensors, an interface and software to provide the simple control language. Or use purpose-made construction kits such as Lego's simple control starter pack.

Conductors and Insulators

Key Idea If a material allows electricity to pass through it we call that material a conductor. If a material does not allow electricity to pass through it we call that material an insulator.

You will need
- Cells and battery holder
- Wire
- Bulb and bulb holder
- Glass, metal, stone, plastic, rubber, wood, paper

1. Predict which of these seven materials are conductors and which are insulators.

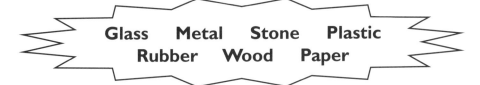

**Glass   Metal   Stone   Plastic
Rubber   Wood   Paper**

2. Set up your experiment as shown below to find out if the materials above are conductors or insulators.

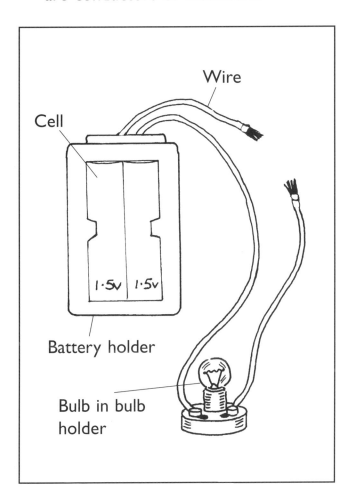

Wire

Cell

1·5v 1·5v

Battery holder

Bulb in bulb holder

3. Touch the wires together to make sure the bulb lights up.

If your bulb does not work

check:

◆ Is the bulb screwed in tightly?

◆ Are the cells the correct way round in the holder?

◆ Are the metal wires twisted tightly on to the holder?

◆ Is the bulb broken?

◆ Are the cells 'dead'? Check by trying a different battery.

4. Now touch the ends of both wires on to each object in turn. Does the bulb light up? Put all the objects that made the bulb light up into one pile. These are conductors. Put all the objects that did not make the bulb light up into another pile. These are insulators.

Looking at Batteries

You will need
- Collection of batteries to include a 1.5V, 4.5V and 9V
- Wires
- Light bulb
- Buzzer
- Motor

Key Idea A battery's power depends on how many volts it has.

1. **a.** Look at your different batteries and write down all the voltage numbers you can see on them.
   b. What is the highest voltage number you can find?
   c. What is the lowest voltage number you can find?

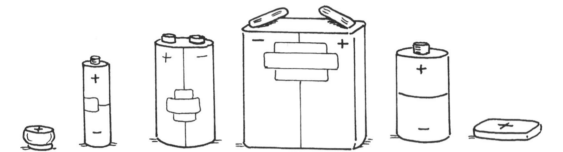

2. Draw each of your batteries and then write the number on each drawing.

3. Construct the three circuits shown below using a 1.5 volt battery, a 4.5 volt battery and a 9 volt battery.

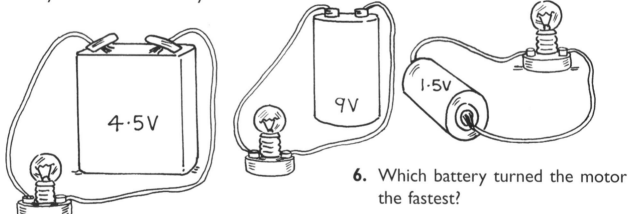

6. Which battery turned the motor the fastest?

7. Now replace the motor with a buzzer and repeat the three circuits.

4. Which circuit had the brightest light bulb?

5. Replace the light bulb with a motor and repeat the three circuits.

8. Which battery made the buzzer have the loudest noise?

 **NOW** Draw a picture of your circuit showing the buzzer that made the loudest noise. Label your picture with the words 'wire', 'battery', 'buzzer'. Write in the number of your battery.
Was it 1.5V, 4.5V or 9V?

Switches

Key Idea A switch closes the gap in a circuit to make a light bulb work.

You will need
- Cells and battery holder
- Light bulb and bulb holder
- Wires
- Card
- Tape
- Foil
- Paperclip
- Two paper fasteners
- Pencil with lead exposed

1. Make a press switch or a sliding switch as shown below and then place it in a circuit to make a light bulb flash on and off.

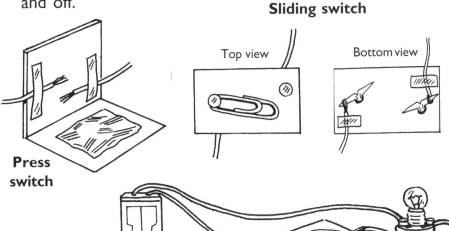

Sliding switch

Top view   Bottom view

Press switch

PRESS

2. Now make a dimmer switch as shown below and place this in your circuit.

Pencil lead is not a metal but is made from a carbon called graphite. It is a conductor of electricity.

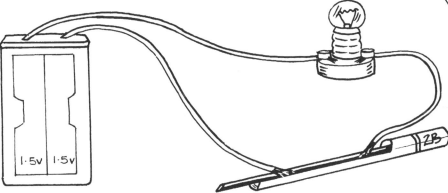

3. Slide the ends of the wire closer together. What happens to the bulb's brightness?

4. Explain how you made your press or sliding switch.

5. Explain how your dimmer switch works.

Circuits

In a circuit, a cell pushes electricity around the wire. The greater the voltage, the greater the push. The amount of electricity that is pushed through the wire depends on how easy it is for the electricity to move through the wire (e.g. how long or thick the wire is, the material the wire is made of, the components joined in the circuit). Electricity always follows the easiest route and will bypass a component if a wire is placed across the component's terminals. When electricity flows through a bulb, the thin twisty filament inside the bulb resists the flow of the electricity. The wire filament gets very hot and glows white (giving light). Remind the children never to connect one end of a cell directly to the other. The electricity will continue to flow and the chemicals in the cell will be used up quickly; the cell will go flat. This is called a short circuit.

Activity pages

Safe Use of Electricity in the Home
Learning objectives
- To know that household electricity is 240V in the UK and is very dangerous.
- To know that short circuits can cause fires.
- To be aware of electrical dangers in the home.

It is important to emphasise to children that household electricity is very dangerous. It is not possible to receive an electric shock from small quantities of electricity using dry cells. However, cells can get extremely hot if the terminals are short-circuited. Warn the children that although water might be considered an insulator, it is in fact a conductor, and will allow high-voltage household electricity to pass through it. They should never touch switches with wet hands.

Arranging Bulbs
Learning objectives
- To know that bulbs can be joined to a battery in different ways.
- To know that when bulbs share a circuit, if one bulb is broken then the others go off.
- To know that if bulbs have their own circuits, if one bulb goes off then the others stay on.

The children do not have to understand the terms 'parallel' and 'series'. They should, however, realise that when bulbs share the same line of wire and one bulb is removed, the circuit becomes broken and all the bulbs will go off. If a number of bulbs are joined to a battery and each has its own circuit, if one bulb is removed then the others can still work. In the series circuits (diagrams f and h) the bulbs will be dim and if one is removed the circuit will be broken and will all go out (as in g and i). In the parallel circuits (diagrams d and e) the bulbs are bright and if one goes out the other remains on.

Electric Quiz Game
Learning objectives
- To know that a circuit must be complete for a bulb to light.
- To be able to build an electric game.

Each of the six wires must be insulated from the others. Use tape or wire that is plastic-covered to prevent short circuits. The ends of the wires need to be exposed as bare metal at each question and answer so the circuit tester can touch them. Use paper clips or paper fasteners to hold the bare wire ends in place.

Oral work

Show what happens to a bulb in a circuit if a wire is placed across the terminals. Place some thin wire across the terminals of a 9V battery. Take care, as the wire will get hot. Explain how this could lead to fires.

Explain the use of metals and plastics in the home in relation to their properties as conductors and insulators.

Discuss what we use electricity for in the home (e.g. heat, motors, sound, light) and discuss the advantages of parallel circuits.

Written work

Ask the children to describe what life would be like without electricity.

Research the discovery by Michael Faraday. How did he make electricity in 1831?

ICT

Show a video on the dangers of mains electricity.

Safe Use of Electricity in the Home

 **Key Idea**   Electricity is potentially dangerous and must be used safely.

1. Look at this circuit. What do you think will happen if a wire is placed across the two terminals of the bulb holder? Why do you think this would happen?

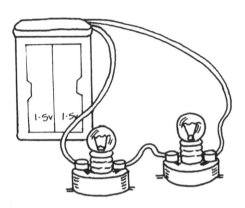 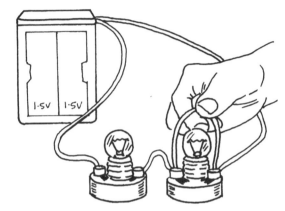

2. Can you find the dangers in each of the following pictures?

 **NOW**   Design a safety poster warning people of the dangers of using electricity in the home.

Arranging Bulbs

Key Idea	The way in which a bulb is attached to a battery affects the performance of that bulb.

You will need
- Cells and battery holder
- Three 1.5V bulbs and bulb holders
- Four wires

1. Look at the nine circuits below.

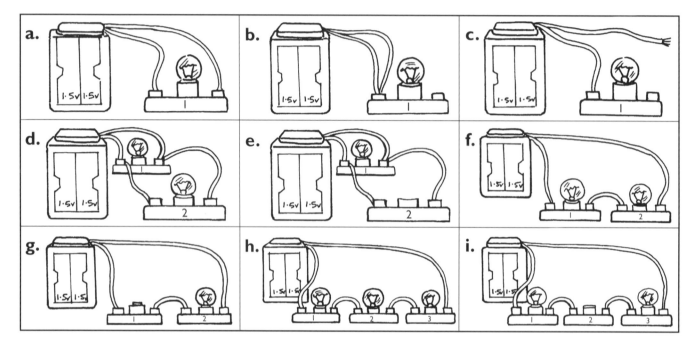

2. Complete part 1 of the table by predicting if the bulbs will light up or stay off in each of the nine experiments. Place a tick in the box if you think the bulb will come on. Place a cross if you think it will not light up.

Circuit	Part 1 My prediction			Part 2 My actual answer		
	Bulb 1	Bulb 2	Bulb 3	Bulb 1	Bulb 2	Bulb 3
a						
b						
c						
d						
e						
f						
g						
h						
i						

3. When you have made your guess, try out each experiment to see if you are correct and then complete part 2 of the table.

Electric Quiz Game

You will need
- Cells and battery holder
- Eight wires
- Light bulb and bulb holder
- Paperclips
- Piece of card

Key Idea

A circuit must be complete for a bulb to light.

1. Set up your circuit tester like this.

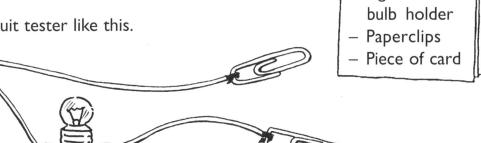

Touch the paper clips together. Your bulb should light up.

2. Design your quiz card. First, draw a table on your piece of card as shown below. You will need five questions and answers. Plan your questions here. Write a question in each box. Write the answers in the other side of the table. Make sure that you jumble up your answers when writing them on the piece of card.

Questions	Answers

3. Attach paperclips next to each question and answer.

4. Turn the card over. Join each question paperclip to its correct answer paperclip by a piece of wire.

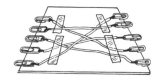

5. Now test out your game. Check that each 'question and answer' circuit is complete. Do this by touching the paper clips for each question and correct answer with your circuit tester. The bulb should light up.

NOW

Try your game out on a friend.

Glossary

Air resistance (pp32, 36) **Force** that slows an object moving through air.

Bimetal thermometer (p12) Thermometer that contains two different metals that are fused together. The metals expand and bend at different temperatures, so pulling to reduce or increase the temperature (for use in thermostatic irons, ovens, etc.).

Bone marrow (p4) Substance in the cavities of bones in which blood cells are produced.

Carbon (pp40, 43) Non-metallic element that occurs naturally as diamond, graphite and charcoal.

Cell (pp40–41, 44) Metal case containing chemicals that can make an electric current. A collection of two or more joined cells makes a battery.

Circuit (pp40, 43–47) Unbroken metal path that lets electricity pass.

Condensation (p20) This happens when steam or water vapour cools and becomes liquid.

Conductor (pp40–41, 44) Material that allows electricity to pass through it.

Dissolve (pp24, 28, 30) Mixed with a liquid and appears to disappear.

Evaporation (pp20, 24, 28, 31) Turning from liquid to gas, for example when water dries.

Fahrenheit (p12) Temperature scale on which freezing equals 32°F and boiling equals 212°F. This scale is named after the German physicist Daniel Fahrenheit (1686–1736).

Filtrate (p24) Substance that has filtered through a porous device such as filter paper.

Force (pp32, 34, 36) Influence that changes the motion of, or produces a stress on, a material/body.

Habitat (p8) Place where things live.

Hibernation (p16) Practice among some animals of spending part of the cold season in a relatively dormant state.

Insulator (pp40–41) Material that does not allow electricity to pass through it.

Invertebrate (p8) Animal without a backbone.

Migration (p16) Regular movement of animals (usually seasonal) from one place to another and then back again.

Optimum body temperature (p16) Most favourable temperature for growth, reproduction, etc.

Saddle (p8) The worm's saddle is used for reproduction. The worm makes a thick ring of slime around its saddle (the thicker part of the worm's body). It lays its eggs in the ring and then adds sperm that it has collected from another worm. It wriggles away from the ring of slime, which turns hard and forms a shell-like cocoon.

Streamlined (pp36–37) When an object has a smooth shape that reduces resistance from, for example, air or water.

Surface area (pp28, 31) Area of the outside of a material.

Tendon (p4) Tissue attaching a muscle to a bone.

Venn diagram (p20) Diagram representing mathematical sets. The diagram is usually in the form of overlapping circles. Intersecting sections contain the elements that the sets have in common.

Volt (pp40, 42, 44) Measure of electrical power. It was named after an Italian scientist called Allesandro Volta (1745–1827), who made many discoveries about electricity. Volt can be shortened to V.

Water resistance (p36) **Force** that slows an object moving through water.